Milk and Mango Take a Trip

글·그림 **미쓔**

미쓔 Missu

영국인 남편을 만나
천사 같은 두 아이와
행복한 일상을 살아가고 있는 아줌마!
그림을 좋아하는 마음 하나로
누구나 도전하면 '나만의 그림책'을
만들 수 있다는 것을 보여주고 싶다.
자신의 일상이 이 세상 가장 특별하고 유일한 이야기임을
깨닫고 많은 이들이 각자의 하루를 모아
마음속에 간직한 소중한 꿈을 이룰 수 있기를 바란다.

∥ 사이트워드(sight words)를 활용한 영어그림책 A Big Blue
Tree 1편에 이어 파닉스 장모음 **a**를 연습하기위한 영어그림책
Milk and Mango Take a Trip 2편입니다. 우유와 망고가 떠난
여행을 따뜻하고 예쁜 그림으로 표현해 보았어요. 우유와 망고
와 함께 부산여행을 떠나볼까요?

∥ 이메일 ajummaonfire@gmail.com
∥ 인스타 instagram.com/ajumma_onfire

주인공 소개

우유(Milk)

작고 하얀 강아지.
성격은 까칠하지만
주인을 잘 따르며 애교가 많다.
망고의 관심을 반기지 않는다.

망고(Mango)

크고 순한 강아지.
노란 털에 근육질 몸매를 자랑한다.
우유를 좋아한다.
하지만 다른 개들이 다가오면
사냥개로 변신한다.

"
반가워,
제주도에 살고 있는 **우유와 망고**라고 해,
우리랑 같이 **재미있게**
영어그림책을 읽어보자고!
"

Contents

Milk and Mango

Step 1

Milk and Mango take a trip to Busan.

They take a plane.

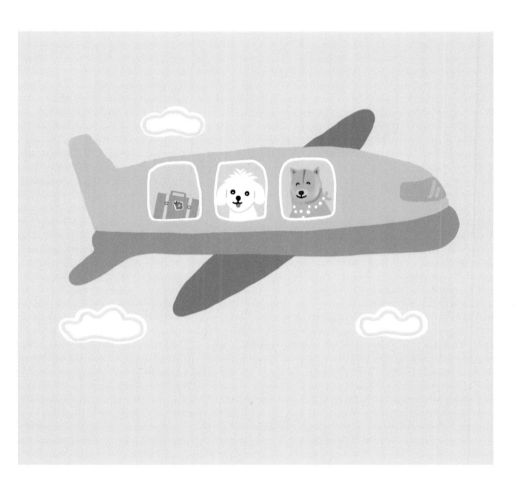

On the plane, they play a game.

Yay, they are in Busan.

They go to Haeundae.

They make a sand snake.

They make a sand cake.

They make a sand grape.

They make a sand ape.

They make a sand snail.

Mango makes a sand jail.

They lay on the sand in the shade.

Milk and Mango Take a Trip

Step 2

It is Sunday.
Milk and Mango want to take a day trip
to Busan.

Will they take a plane?
Will they take a train?
Will they sail?

They will take a plane.
They wait for the plane.

On the plane, they play a game.

Yay, they are in Busan.

They go to Haeundae.

They get a spade.
They make a sand snake.

They make a sand cake.

They make a sand grape.

They make a sand ape.

They make a sand snail.

Mango makes a sand jail.

They chase birds.

They play in the waves.

They lay on the sand in the shade.
It was a great day.

Milk and Mango Take a Trip to Busan

Step 3

It is Sunday.
Milk and Mango want to take a day trip
to Busan.

Will they take a plane?
Will they take a train?
Will they sail?

They will take a plane.
They pay for the ticket and
wait for the plane.
They wait for the plane.

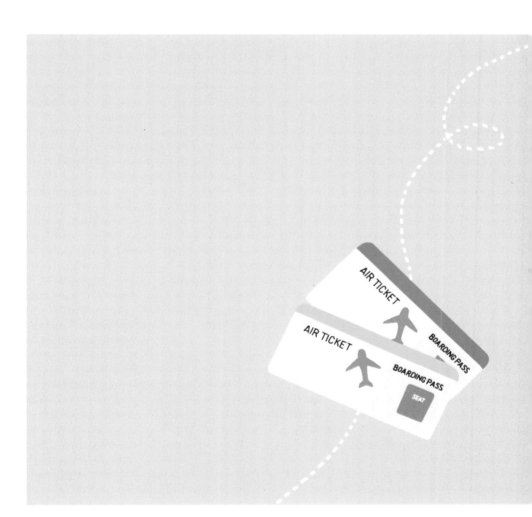

On the plane, they play a game.

Yay, they are in Busan.
They race to the subway.
They go to Haeundae.

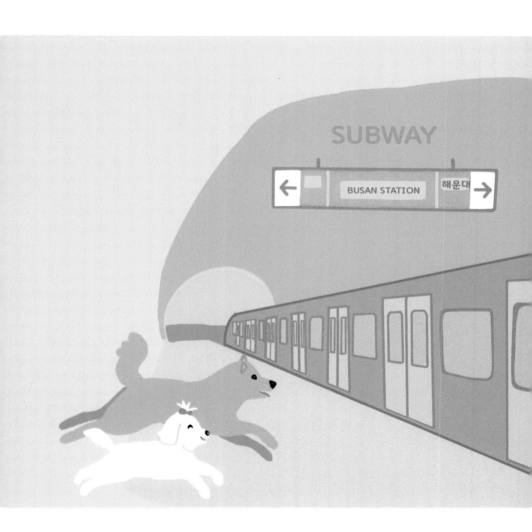

Look, it is gray.
What is it?
Oh no, it is rain.
They hate rain.

Wait!
Yay, it is the sun.
Look, it is a rainbow.

They get a spade.
They make a sand snake.

They make a sand cake.

They make a sand grape.

They make a sand ape.

They make a sand snail.

Mango makes a sand jail.

They chase birds.

They play in the waves.

Look! A whale, aaaah.

They lay on the sand in the shade.
It was a great day.

Oh no, they are late.
They race to the subway.
They pray.
Yes, there is a delay.
They are not late.

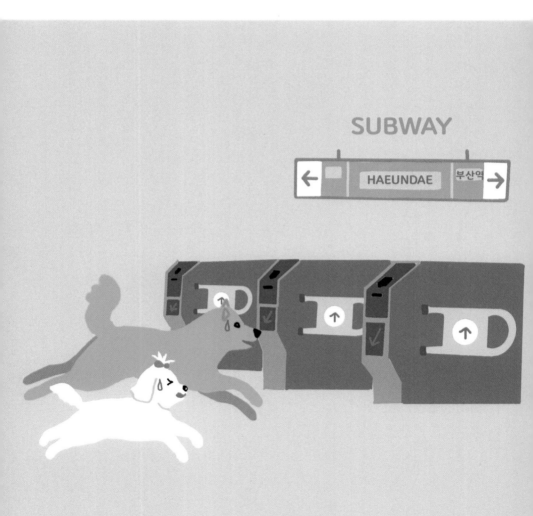

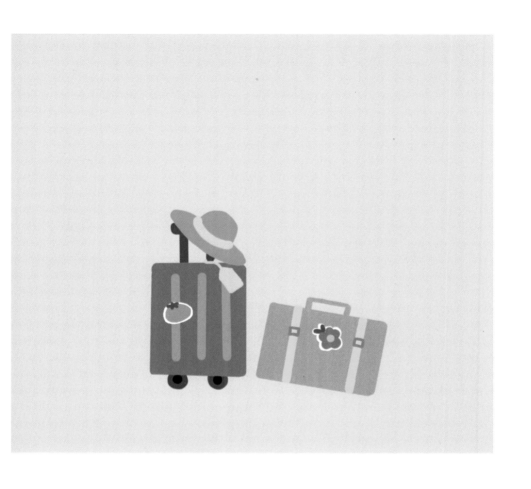

It was a great day.

Milk and Mango Take a Trip
ⓒ미쓔 2024

발행 2024년 07월 23일

지은이 미쓔
펴낸이 한건희
펴낸곳 (주)부크크
출판등록 2014년 7월 15일(제2014-16호)
주소 서울특별시 금천구 가산디지털1로 119 SK트윈타워 A동 305호
전화 1670-8316
이메일 info@bookk.co.kr

ISBN 979-11-410-9669-4

www.bookk.co.kr